The Boy Who Loved All Living Things

The Imaginary Childhood Journal of Albert Schweitzer

Sheila Hamanaka

Animal Welfare Institute

ISBN: 0-938414-98-4

Library of Congress Control Number: 2006938591

Published by:

Animal Welfare Institute

P.O. Box 3650

Washington, D.C. 20027

www.awionline.org

Designed by Will Mangum

In loving memory of my mother

Mary Fumi Kusano Sasaki

who taught me to be kind to animals

The Boy Who Loved All Living Things

The Imaginary Childhood Journal of Albert Schweitzer

Sheila Hamanaka

There are more children born every month than there are hairs on a tiger's back. And each one has courage. This is the story of an especially brave child who was born long ago, in 1875, in a small country called Alsace.

Of course, there are many such children, and they can be found in every country, large or small. In fact, you might be one of them...

The especially brave boy was named Albert. When he grew up, he became a famous doctor, musician, minister and philosopher. In 1952, he won the Nobel Peace Prize. What made Albert such a special child? He never made a scrapbook or wrote a journal when he was a little boy.

But if he had, perhaps it would look like this...

Hello.
My name is Albert. And
these are some of my friends ...

I especially love 🐷 pigs!
When I grow up, I want a big
herd of

These are my friends at school. I <u>hate</u> to wear
fancy clothes! The poor village boys make fun of me.

Father

Mother

My mother made me a  coat, but I will not wear it. Father got angry and hit me! He even locked me in the cellar, but still I will <u>not</u> wear it. I want to be like the other village boys!

My father is a minister.
My little friends live in
every nook and cranny
of our church!

My father plays piano. He is teaching me! And soon I will play the organ at church. I will play songs without words just as my bird friends do when they fly around.

When I play music, I feel like I am flying, too!

I think about my friends a lot. I say my prayers every night when I go to bed. But no one prays for my friends.

So I have added these words:
Protect and bless all living things. Keep them free from evil, and let them sleep in peace.

I say this secretly every night.

I cannot sleep! Today I saw two men beating an old horse. She knew where they were dragging her – to the slaughter house! She has spent her whole life pulling a heavy cart. Is this her reward? How can people be so mean to animals?!!

I keep thinking about that poor horse!
And now I must confess –
I have been stupid and cruel myself.
Once I hit my dog with a stick
to stop him from
chasing someone, instead of
holding his collar. I did it because it
made me feel big and strong. I thought he would
hate me but instead he forgave me and
covered me with dog kisses!
Now I feel ashamed.
Another confession – I
got to drive a carriage
pulled by an old horse. I
hit him with a whip to
make him run faster!

I felt like I was racing a chariot. In the end, the horse was tired and gasping for air. He hung his head and would not look at me. I said I was sorry, but what good are words? Why did I have to act like such a show off? How could I be so cruel to an old horse?!

Day by day I am kinder to my animal friends. Even Worms!

Today I told my friends I don't want to go fishing. Look at this hook. Ouch!!!

It is pointy and sharp and it kills the worms and hurts the fish. They have feelings too!

They said, "You are right!" So we went to the woods to find something better to do. I waved Good-bye to my fish friends.

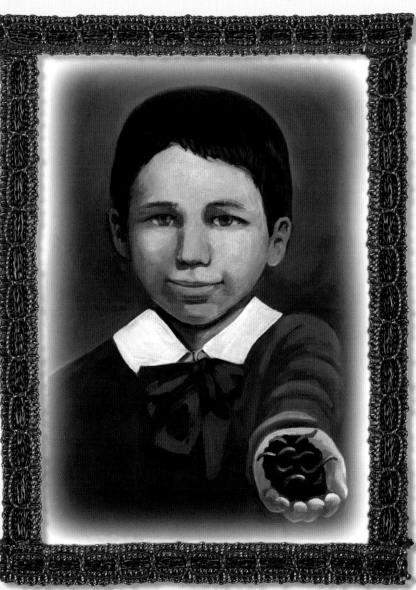

Today I faced a big test! Heinrich and I had made slingshots. He said to me "Let's go shoot some birds." I hated the idea, but I went with him anyway. We stood under a tree that was filled with birds. "Get a rock," he said, "we can each kill a bird. You're not afraid, are you, Albert?"

I was afraid. I was afraid Heinrich would laugh at me if I refused to shoot.

The birds were not scared of me. After all, I was their friend. They kept singing our song without words

I picked up a rock. I decided I would shoot, but miss the birds.

But Heinrich did not want to miss!
He took aim ...

Just at that second, the
church bells began to ring!!!

I threw down my slingshot and chased
the birds away to save them from Heinrich!
The church bells seemed to ring out the
words, "Thou shalt not Kill."

I do not care anymore
what people think
about me!

I know
deep inside

who I am.

I am a boy who loves all living things.
And I have many friends!

Albert Schweitzer grew up to be a famous man.

He could have stayed in Alsace and lived a comfortable life giving sermons and playing the organ. Instead, he went back to school to become a doctor. Then he built a clinic in a village called Lambarane, deep in the forests of Gabon, Africa, where he felt he was needed the most. People thought he was crazy, because at that time most of Europe only wanted to profit from Africa's riches. Most Europeans did not care that millions of African people were dying because they were being treated like slaves.

Albert had many four-legged and feathered friends at the clinic and he became a vegetarian because he loved animals. He did not care what other people thought about him.

He had learned as a boy who he was.

He was a man who loved all living things.

And he had many friends.

THE ANIMAL WELFARE INSTITUTE

The Animal Welfare Institute (AWI) was started in 1951 by Christine Stevens, a woman who was much like Albert Schweitzer: she loved animals. AWI works hard to protect animals from pain and fear. AWI educates people about animals and their suffering. We ask Members of Congress to pass laws to benefit animals in need. We try to help all animals — including those in experimental laboratories, on factory farms, caught in steel traps set in the woods, and threatened with extinction — from the smallest mice to the great whales in the sea.

For more information, visit the AWI website:
www.awionline.org

THE ALBERT SCHWEITZER AWARD

The Animal Welfare Institute presents the Albert Schweitzer Medal to a person who has done outstanding work to help animals. Albert and his dog Tchu Tchu appear in the medal, along with Albert's words:

"We need a boundless ethics which will include the animals also."